THE WISDOM OF
WOODSTOCK

CHARLES M. SCHULZ

RUNNING PRESS
PHILADELPHIA

WOODSTOCK WANTS TO FLY TO DISTANT HORIZONS BUT HE DOESN'T KNOW WHERE THEY ARE
SIGH

BOOT!

WELL, PERHAPS I CAN CLEAR UP A LITTLE MISCONCEPTION FOR YOU

SNOWSTORMS ARE NOT CAUSED BY KICKING A SNOWMAN!
WHEW
SIGH

MOBILE HOME

?
SIGH
I HATE PLAYING "BAT"!

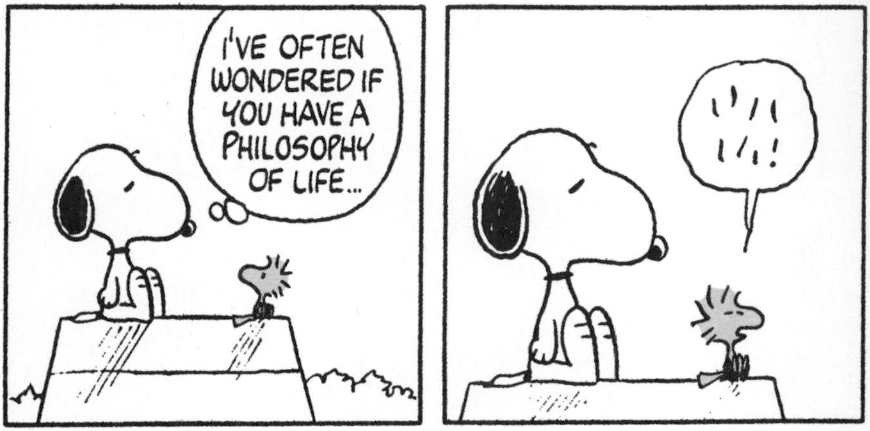
I'VE OFTEN WONDERED IF YOU HAVE A PHILOSOPHY OF LIFE...

I MIGHT HAVE KNOWN...
"SMALL IS BEAUTIFUL!"

DEAR SIR..
KLUNK!
SECRETARIES AREN'T WORTH MUCH ON MONDAY MORNINGS

IT IS NOW TEN MINUTES AFTER ONE
IT IS NOW ONE-THIRTY...
IT IS NOW ONE-FORTY-FIVE...
BONK!
ON TUESDAYS, SECRETARIES ARE ALWAYS LATE GETTING BACK FROM LUNCH...

AHEM!

EVERY NOW AND THEN HE TRIES TO PUT IN TOO MUCH DETAIL!

WOODSTOCK'S STORIES ALWAYS START OFF GOOD, BUT THEN THEY GET VERY SAD...

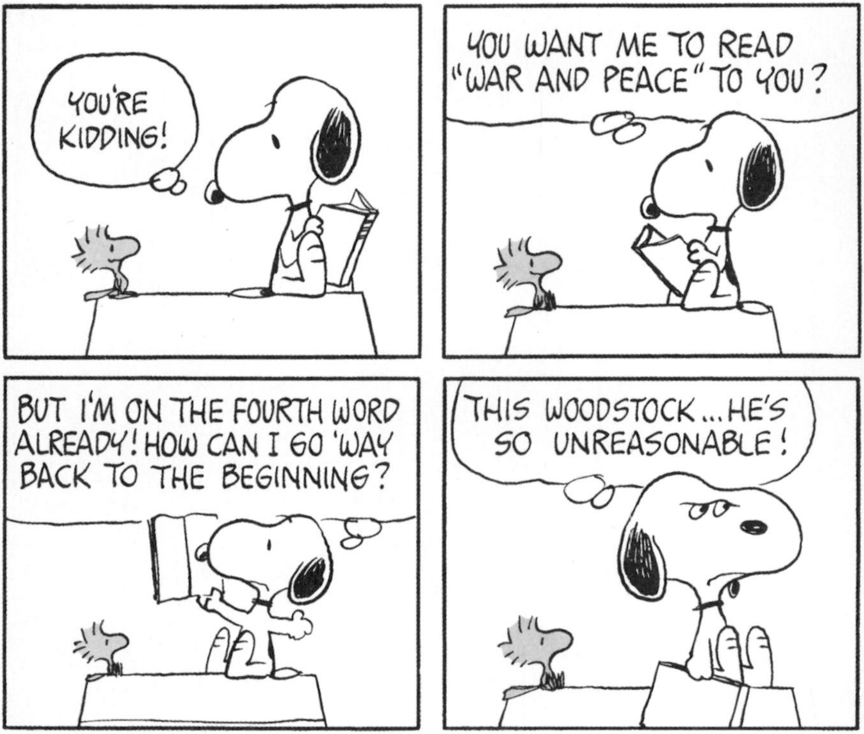
YOU'RE KIDDING!
YOU WANT ME TO READ "WAR AND PEACE" TO YOU?
BUT I'M ON THE FOURTH WORD ALREADY! HOW CAN I GO 'WAY BACK TO THE BEGINNING?
THIS WOODSTOCK... HE'S SO UNREASONABLE!

"'AND.'"
?
THAT WAS IT! "AND"! I'M ONLY READING ONE WORD A DAY..THAT WAS IT..."AND"!!
DON'T TELL ME HOW TO READ "WAR AND PEACE"!

WOODSTOCK? ON A SKATEBOARD?
THAT STUPID BIRD... HE CAN'T RIDE A SKATEBOARD...

HE'LL KILL HIMSELF...

BONK!

I CAN'T BELIEVE IT!
WOODSTOCK HAS FALLEN IN LOVE WITH A WORM!

I CAN'T BELIEVE IT..

THAT'S LIKE ME FALLING IN LOVE WITH A CAN OF DOG FOOD

IT'S MIGRATING TIME...
THIS IS THE TIME OF YEAR WHEN MILLIONS OF BIRDS ARE TAKING OFF FOR WARMER CLIMATES...

ALL BUT WOODSTOCK, WHO'S AFRAID OF GETTING MUGGED!
SIGH

THAT'S THE WORST EXCUSE
I'VE EVER HEARD!
SIGH!

ON WEDNESDAYS, SECRETARIES WORK VERY HARD..
type type type
THEY RUSH HERE AND THERE DOING THIS AND THAT..
..AND THEY ACCOMPLISH GREAT THINGS..
type type type type DING!
..ON WEDNESDAYS, THAT IS!

TELEPHONE!
I'LL BET I KNOW WHAT IT IS..
I KNEW IT..
102°
ON THURSDAYS, SECRETARIES ALWAYS CALL IN SICK..

BOOT!

boot!

HOW'S THIS ONE?
X
RATS!
X!
HOW ABOUT THIS ONE?
X!
THEN HOW ABOUT THIS ONE?
X!

IT'S IMPOSSIBLE TO GO FISHING WITH WOODSTOCK.. HE KNOWS ALL THE WORMS PERSONALLY!

I ORDERED A TOY BICYCLE FOR YOUR DOLL SET, BUT IT NEVER CAME...
I HAVE A FEELING IT WAS PROBABLY DELIVERED TO THE WRONG ADDRESS...
WELL, I HOPE WHOEVER GOT IT, ENJOYS IT!!
WHEELIES, YET! GOOD GRIEF!

HERE COMES WOODSTOCK ON HIS NEW BICYCLE...
I HATE IT WHEN HE SAYS, "LOOK, NO WINGS!"

HE SAID I WAS VIOLATING HIS BODY SPACE!

Z
Z
HE'S A LONG WAY FROM BEING READY FOR TELEPHONE WIRES...

WHEN YOU'RE YOUNG, YOU THINK A LOT ABOUT THE FUTURE
YOU THINK ABOUT LIFE...
YOU THINK A LOT ABOUT WHAT YOU HOPE YOU'LL BE..
WOODSTOCK WANTS TO BE AN EAGLE

?
???
IT'S CALLED A "PUMPKIN"

TONIGHT IS HALLOWEEN .. ALL THE PUMPKINS YOU SEE TONIGHT ARE FILLED WITH GHOSTS!

WOODSTOCK IS SEARCHING FOR HIS IDENTITY
WE KNOW HE'S NOT AN EAGLE BECAUSE HE CAN'T STAND HEIGHTS
ANOTHER THING HE'S NOT IS A DUCK!
!

POOR WOODSTOCK...WORMS ARE ALWAYS PICKING ON HIM
!

THANKSGIVING IS A BAD TIME TO BE A BIRD...

WOOF!

WHY DO BIRDS NEED SO MUCH STRING WHEN THEY'RE BUILDING A NEST ?

I'M SURE I DON'T KNOW

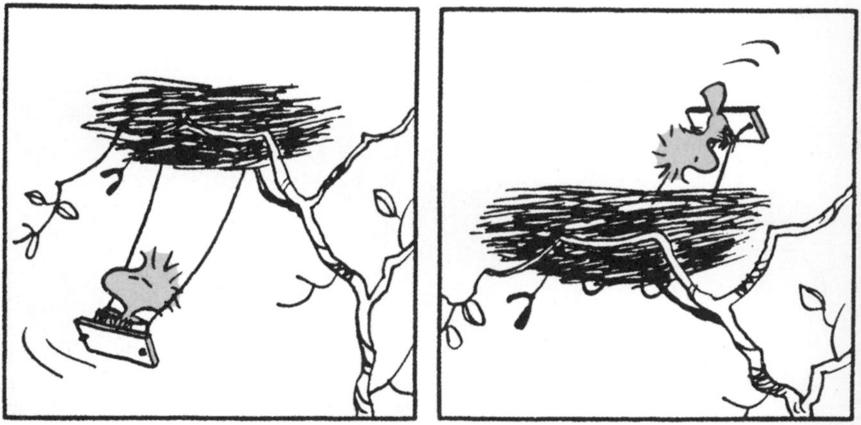

I HATE IT WHEN HE PLAYS "ELEVATOR"!

WOODSTOCK THINKS THAT IF YOU SIT IN A MAILBOX LONG ENOUGH, YOU'LL GET A CHRISTMAS CARD... HE'S SO NAIVE... HE JUST..

WOODSTOCK GIVES BORING PARTIES!

He is truly a good dog.
type type type
He is also a loyal friend.

Therefore, I would like to recommend ol' banana nose for Neighborhood Dog of the Year.
HEE HEE HEE HEE HEE HEE

type type type
DING!
type type type
type DING!
ZIP! BANG!
RATTLE RATTLE!
type type
type type
DING!
type type type type DING!
fold fold fold, lick lick!
stamp stamp!
type type
?!*?! ZIP!
type type DING!
ON FRIDAY AFTERNOONS AT FOUR O'CLOCK, SECRETARIES MAKE A LOT OF NOISE!
ZOOM!

Z
Z
Z
AND ON SATURDAYS, SECRETARIES SLEEP 'TIL NOON!

Z

TELEPHONE

WOODSTOCK HAS NEVER SEEN A VIOLIN OR A FIRE TRUCK OR A CANDY STORE..
HE'S NEVER HEARD AN OPERA OR A SYMPHONY... HE'S NEVER SEEN A MOVIE OR A PLAY...

ON THE OTHER HAND, HE'S SEEN THE SKY, THE CLOUDS, THE GROUND, THE SUN, THE RAIN, THE MOON, THE STARS, A CAT AND SEVERAL WORMS...
WOODSTOCK FEELS THAT HE'S LED A VERY FULL LIFE!

A PELICAN?